D0189423

Further excellent Murder Mysteries available from
Lagoon Books:

DEATH IN THE FAMILY
(ISBN 1899712496)

MURDER ON THE RIVIERA EXPRESS
(ISBN 189971247X)

MURDER IN MANHATTAN
(ISBN 1899712488)

60 SECOND MURDER PUZZLES
(ISBN 1899712453)

All books can be ordered from bookshops by quoting the
ISBN number shown.

Death
after
Dinner

A *Mystery*

PUZZLE BOOK

LAGOON
BOOKS

YOU ARE THE DETECTIVE!

Series Editor: Simon Melhuish
Editor: Heather Dickson
Author: Nick Hoare
Page design and layout: Gary Sherwood & Gary Inwood Studios
Cover design, photography & illustrations : Gary Sherwood

Published by:
LAGOON BOOKS
PO BOX 311, KT2 5QW, UK

ISBN: 1899712461

INTRODUCTION

You are a detective - not just any detective, but one of the greatest sleuths in the country. You are due to retire in just four weeks time, with an untarnished history of solved crimes behind you. In the meantime you just want to lie low and take it easy. The last thing you want is a tricky case that might just spoil your excellent reputation...

Unfortunately a cloud has appeared on the horizon, in the form of a dossier of information from the police in the quiet residential suburb of Forley. Local luxury holiday co-ordinator Harry Hilton has been found dead in his home, following a dinner party. Knowing that the vast majority of such crimes are solved almost immediately, you are initially puzzled as to why this has been passed on to you. As you start to leaf through the file, however, you begin to see that this is not just another open-and-shut case. Far from it. The local police are sure it's murder but are clueless as to who did it. They want you to come down and spend ten days helping them solve it.

Most of the hard work has been done. All you need to do to solve the mystery and claim all the praise, is read the following police dossier on the case. And then you can retire with your record unblemished.

But will it be that simple?

Index

USEFUL TIPS

All the information except the actual interviews with the six
suspects is 100% accurate. Whether or not it is relevant, or
particularly helpful, to your detective work is another matter
altogether.

The murderer is not necessarily the only person who is lying.
Other suspects may have done things which they do not
want to admit, so they might lie to cover their actions.

The murderer acted alone. Other suspects may well have
had motives for killing the deceased, or may well point the
finger at someone they think did it, but no one except the
murderer and hopefully yourself, by the time you have read
the book, know who is guilty.

The local police, in the form of Detective Inspector Ken
Rogers, are fallible. If they weren't, they wouldn't need your
help. Throughout the book there are times when Rogers will
assess the new developments.

Before reading these it is best to make your own notes.
Rogers has so far failed to solve the case, you don't want him
to mislead or confuse you.

In order to solve the mystery, you are advised to take notes
while you read the book.

Remember, this is your case and you want your retirement
bonus to reflect your success.

Good luck.

FORLEY BUGLE

30th August 1996

LOCAL BUSINESSMAN BLUDGEONED TO DEATH

EXCLUSIVE by Mark Dyer

LUXURY tour co-ordinator Harry Hilton was found bludgeoned to death last night at his home at 59 Kippax Grove. Mr Hilton, 31, who had been giving a dinner party for close friends and neighbours, was found in his study by his ex-girlfriend Miranda Davies. Visibly shocked and clearly upset by the death of her former boyfriend, Miss Davies, a top solicitor with international finance house Slater Gibson Franzosich, said Hilton had left the dinner table at just after 10.20pm and retired to his study. She told *The Bugle* that as he did not reappear, she went to look for him at around 11.35pm. She found him slumped across his desk in his upstairs study.

Cont. on page 9

LOCAL BUSINESSMAN BLUDGEONED TO DEATH Continued

EXCLUSIVE by Mark Dyer

He was taken to Forley General where he was confirmed dead on arrival. Police investigating the case believe the victim was hit on the head with a blunt instrument. Although they have yet to charge anyone with his murder, everyone who attended the dinner was detained for questioning. Detective Inspector Ken Rogers of Forley CID said:"While we have yet to eliminate a number of possible suspects, we are confident that the root of this terrible crime was domestic, and that we will shortly bring the killer to justice." One guest, believed to be cellist Antonia Curbishley, who lives in the top floor flat at Number 59 Kippax Grove, was detained in hospital overnight suffering from shock.

Other guests present on the fateful evening included Harry Hilton's next door neighbours and his school friend Antony Croton, son of the MP for Forley East Leonard Croton OBE.

Scene of Crime

Scene of Crime Report 1

Date: 29th August

Time on scene: 23:55hrs

Offence: Murder.

Victim: Harold Bertram Hilton
male, 31 years.

Perpetrator: Unknown.

Location: 59 Kippax Grove,
Forley FW4 8UG.

Description:
Body located in study (first floor).
Found seated in chair, slumped over the
desk. Telephone receiver in left hand.
Jade statuette, heavily bloodstained
(source as yet unidentified) found on
floor behind victim. Wounds suggest this
was the weapon.

Cause of Death:
Two or three blows to the head with a
heavy blunt instrument.

First to Scene:
Miranda Davies

Time: 23:35hrs

Possible Suspects:

Miranda Davies (F) 30,
deceased's former girlfriend, co-habitee
of main flat, 59 Kippax Grove. No
previous convictions.

Antony Croton (M) 30,
also resident in main flat. Currently
"seeking employment". No record, but was
cautioned for funding trip to Far East and
Australasia with father's credit cards.

Desmond Thruxton (M) 57,
deceased's next door neighbour (61 Kippax
Grove). Previous conviction for drunk and
disorderly after incident at the Bower
restaurant, the day after he had been
given his notice there.

Shirley Thruxton (F) 44,
wife of Desmond Thruxton. No previous
convictions.

Karl Wilson (M) 39,
resident in basement flat at 59 Kippax
Grove. Librarian at Geoff Street public
library. Previous convictions for breach
of the peace, all at demonstrations and
picket lines outside mines, laboratories
and politicians' houses. Served six weeks
in 1983 after pleading guilty to causing
affray. A charge of assaulting an
officer was dropped.

Antonia Curbishley (F) 35,
resident in top flat 59 Kippax Grove.
No previous convictions. Needed minor
treatment for injury sustained to hand at
crime scene. She was retained in
hospital for overnight observation, due to
highly distressed state.

Officer on Scene: Detective Inspector
Ken Rogers

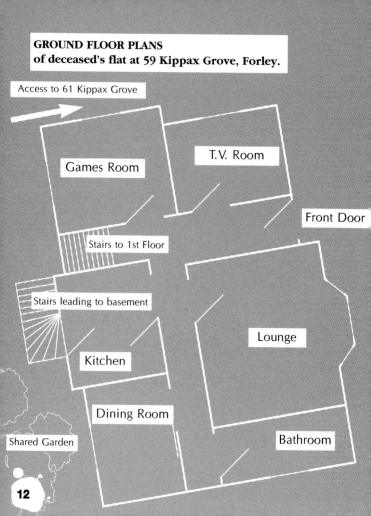

GROUND FLOOR PLANS
of deceased's flat at 59 Kippax Grove, Forley.

Access to 61 Kippax Grove

Games Room

T.V. Room

Front Door

Stairs to 1st Floor

Stairs leading to basement

Kitchen

Lounge

Dining Room

Shared Garden

Bathroom

12

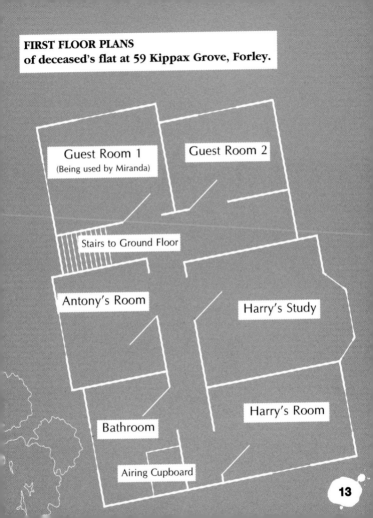

FIRST FLOOR PLANS
of deceased's flat at 59 Kippax Grove, Forley.

Guest Room 1
(Being used by Miranda)

Guest Room 2

Stairs to Ground Floor

Antony's Room

Harry's Study

Harry's Room

Bathroom

Airing Cupboard

13

Miranda Davies
Age 30.

Deceased's flatmate and ex-girlfriend.
She is an extremely successful solicitor with Slater
Gibson Franzosich, an international finance house.
They met each other on a year-off trip to Australia
and were the epitome of "bright young things" at
Oxford. They split up nine months before Harry's
murder and Miranda had been about to
move out into the flat she bought as
an investment four years earlier.
The split was sufficiently
amicable for them to
carry on sharing a flat
although friends had
witnessed a slight
increase in tension
recently. When asked,
both of them would say
that there were very good
financial reasons for
continuing to share.

Miranda has a pathological hatred of being deceived. Aged five, she refused to speak to her father for eighteen months when she discovered the truth about Santa Claus. She recently slapped one of her oldest friends around the face during an after dinner game of "Call My Bluff". She has told Harry that he would be "incredibly stupid and unreservedly sorry" if he ever lied to her again.

Antony Croton
Age 30.

He met the deceased at public school, and they have been close friends ever since. He is also resident in the main flat. Academically poor, his career, such as it is, has seen him flit between jobs arranged for him by his parents and their friends, never really making his mark at any of them. He was rejected by the Household Cavalry, his father's regiment, on the grounds of being "physically and mentally unsuitable". Currently seeking employment, he was made redundant by Harry six weeks ago. Harry had involved him in Exclusively Jet Set, his travel company, from the beginning, but had had to lay him off due to "down-sizing". Since then he has done little other than "lunch" and visit an ever-dwindling circle of contacts, the pool of easy-to-do, hard-to-foul-up jobs seemed to have dried up.

Antony only managed to persuade Harry to give him
the administration assistant position at Exclusively Jet Set
by offering him £5,000 from his trust fund as an
"investment". Before accepting it,
Harry had his solicitor draw up an agreement that
made the investment strictly non-refundable.

Desmond Thruxton
Age 57.

A neighbour of the deceased.
He and his wife have lived in Kippax Grove for eight
years. Desmond is a chef who, early in his career,
looked destined to make it to the
very crest of the culinary wave.
However, he found himself falling
from favour at restaurant after
restaurant, and as the grapevine
began to work against him, he
found it more and more difficult
to get any sort of work in top
restaurants. He was the chef at a
small suburban French restaurant
in Forley itself, until an
"unsightly incident", involving
"unacceptable" behaviour,
caused him to be shown his cards.

Desmond is terrified of catching diseases from blood. At work, he washes his hands constantly when handling meat, making him a figure of fun in the kitchen.

Shirley Thruxton
Age 44.

A neighbour of the deceased, she met her husband
Desmond while she was waitressing in a restaurant
where he was working. Now she runs a thriving
agency which provides staff for high class
restaurants and hotels. Her career has been as much
of a success as her husband's has been a failure. The
difference in fortune, combined with different
working hours and a 13 year age
gap has driven them apart. She
supports him, and has no plans
to divorce him, but they have
recently been sleeping in
separate rooms.

As her relationship with her husband crumbled, Shirley developed a "thing" for younger men.

Karl Wilson
Age 39.

Karl (born Charles) has lived in the basement flat
since before Harry bought the building and
complained bitterly about the rent increases that
Harry introduced. Purporting to have been "born a
communist", Karl has lent his support to numerous
causes over the years. Working as a librarian for the
local labour council is one of the few jobs that he
could permit himself to do.
He shops and eats with
care, refusing to buy
anything which could
oppress or disadvantage
any group of people and/
or animals through its
supply and production.

Karl has told his friends that come the revolution, Harry would be the first up against the wall, and that he would volunteer to pull the trigger. Recently, he confided to Samantha, his partner, that he might not be able to wait for the revolution.

Antonia Curbishley
Age 35.

The deceased's top floor flat neighbour.
Antonia is a cellist by profession, although she had to
give up her position with a successful touring
orchestra due to ill health and her rather fragile
constitution. For the past few months she has been
at home, recovering from what she describes as her
"little bit of a turn", practising her cello and teaching
piano and music theory to children.
Her lack of full time work has
greatly reduced her income,
and at times she has had
difficulty making ends meet.
She had run-ins with the
deceased regarding rent as
well as the noise
(hers during the day,
his late at night).

Antonia may appear to be quite frail, but years of lugging a cello around, coupled with the women's self-defence class she goes to once a week, has made her deceptively strong.

Detective Inspector Rogers and Miranda Davies.

Tell me what happened on the night in question, the events leading up to your discovery of the body.

Well, everyone came for dinner. I mean, Karl from downstairs, Antonia from the attic, and the Thruxtons from next door. And me and Tony, of course.

You say "everyone". Did all seven of you often do things together?

God, no! It...it just seemed the right time.

The right time for what?

Harry had been very busy, particularly since he'd had to let Tony go, and, besides that, there....there had been one or two little problems with the neighbours, so Harry, God bless him, thought the easiest way of sorting it all out was to cook everyone an expensive dinner, and then they'd all forget whatever it was that had been upsetting them. Dealing with people wasn't one of his strong points you see.

So he cooked this meal, and...

He didn't even cook it himself. He got Desmond from next door in to do it...as a favour, or in return for something, I think. Anyhow, everyone turns up, and it's all a bit awkward. Nobody has anything in common, and Harry, Tony and I hadn't been getting along famously since Harry and I split up and Harry sacked Tony. But then everyone got stuck into this case of wine Harry had been sent by one of the hotels he dealt with.

And this improved things?

Not really. Well, for a bit, maybe, but then it all fell apart. I imagine it was all a bit bourgeois for Karl, but then virtually everything is for him. Even under the best of circumstances he and Harry wouldn't get on, but with all this to-do over rent and so on, it just got worse. He's one of those people who just seems determined to have a rotten time and to hate everything. And there's something very creepy about him. And he...I know it's awful to say it, but he smells. He always wears that combat jacket and those boots. Harry made a joke about it, you know, "No need to dress up, old man", that sort of thing and then Karl started spouting off about how clothes are the chains that enslave the suburban middle classes. He's awful. He gives me the creeps.

What can you tell me about the injury to Miss Curbishley?

Oh dear, that was terrible. Antonia has had a lot of problems, I think. She's very over-sensitive, and Harry could be incredibly insensitive, particularly after a few glasses of wine. She'd lost her cat, it got run over a couple of weeks ago, and Harry made a joke about cats, and she started screaming, and hitting the table with her knife.

All this after one joke about cats?

Well, a couple, from Tony too. But she really over-reacted. There was no malice in it. Not really. We were just about to have coffee when she suddenly went really manic, stabbed the table three times and must have caught her hand with the knife. There was blood everywhere.

What happened after that?

Well, Harry left the table. He said he had work to do, and he usually did, but I think he realised that it had all backfired.

He didn't try to apologise to Antonia, or make it up to her?

No, of course not. You don't start screaming and stabbing yourself at dinner parties just because the host cracks a joke about cats you know.

What did you do at this point?

I was trying to stop the bleeding and calm her down. Desmond, Desmond Thruxton was helping me. It's the sort of thing that happens in kitchens all the time, apparently.

What were the others doing?

Karl left in disgust. I'm sure if Antonia had been a miner, injured by a drill, that would have been OK, but it was a "stupid bourgeois self-indulgence". To be fair, he was furious with Harry, too. He's big on animals. We sent Antony off to find a bottle of brandy, but he was gone for ages.

When was this?

Well, she cut herself at about 10.20pm, and this was about five minutes after. Harry and Karl had already left by the time he went.

You said he was gone for ages. Roughly how long is that?

About ten minutes or so. Antonia was still in quite a state, so Shirley went next door to get her a tranquilliser or something.

Did she leave by the front door?

I think she went through the garden. Saves having to unlock both front doors. She was gone a while. Of course Antony reappeared with some brandy almost immediately after she'd left. Desmond tried to phone her next door, to tell her not to bother looking, but her phone was engaged.

Did you leave Antonia at any point?

Yes. I went to the kitchen to get a clean tea-towel to bind her cut.

Did you find one?

No. No, I didn't. I went upstairs to see if we had any bandages in the bathroom. We didn't, so I got a tea-towel from the airing cupboard.

You didn't see Harry at this point?

No, his office door was shut. But I did hear him talking, on the phone, I suppose. I got back downstairs at 11, the clock was chiming, you see, and I dressed the wound with Desmond's help. Then Antonia, who'd had about quarter of a bottle of brandy by this stage, went to the bathroom to clean herself up a bit.

And you didn't leave the room until you discovered the body?

No, I was going to try to get Harry to speak to her. She was much, much calmer after cleaning herself up, but she kept on saying "I'm fine" and "Calm, calm, calm" to herself, so she still wasn't quite right. I went up to Harry's office at about 11.35pm. I burst in, turned the main light on and found him slumped on the desk covered in blood. It was that bastard Karl, I know it was. After the ambulance had taken Harry away, Karl said he'd seen him on the phone minutes earlier. He did it, I'm sure he did it....

(Interview terminated due to extreme distress of interviewee.)

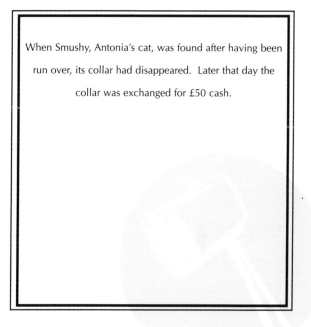

When Smushy, Antonia's cat, was found after having been run over, its collar had disappeared. Later that day the collar was exchanged for £50 cash.

Detective Inspector Rogers and Antony Croton.

What can you tell me about the dinner party that preceded the murder?

Awful. Simply awful. Wrong mix, you see. Have to have the right mix. Like cocktails, you see. Except they're not drinks of course.

Did Harry annoy or upset anyone in particular?

Antonia, obviously. Lots of cracks about cellists, you know, that Thomas Beacham one about scratching an instrument of pleasure. Sorry. He could be very mean Harry. But he was very good at getting people to laugh at things which were cruel. There were lots of jokes about cats too, which were beyond the pale. Poor woman was obviously unbalanced.

Anyone else?

The cellar dweller didn't look very....

Cellar dweller?

Sorry, I mean Karl. It's just a nickname. He was getting a bit steamed up, but I didn't pay much attention. He was always angry about something. Chalk and cheese, him and Harry. The whole idea of inviting all these people who didn't like each other, to "patch things up", ridiculous really. Particularly Karl. It's not just the class thing, it's...it...have you spoken to Miranda about this?

She has been interviewed. Why is that relevant?
Oh, it's just that...well, one doesn't like to point the finger without having all the evidence, you lot must know all about that sort of thing, but...erm...it...it's a little delicate, you see.

I appreciate that, but I must remind you that this is a murder investigation. It is essential I know everything.

Of course it is. For a couple of months, some rather strange things have been happening, happening to Miranda, if you see what I mean.

What sort of things?

Oh, you know. Certain items of clothing have gone missing from the washing line, intimate items, if you get my drift. A couple of weeks ago she was having a shower when she realised that someone was outside the window, looking in. Other times she's seen someone watching her in the garden when she's been getting ready for bed. Then there were a couple of anonymous letters, not threatening or anything, just proclaiming undying love. Creepy, don't you think?

She told you about this?

From the beginning. Me and Harry thought it was hilarious, thought she was round the twist. It was only when she got the letters that we realised it was real. We still thought it was really funny, although I don't think Randa thought so. We thought about ways of catching him. Harry even got all this stuff from one of the safari companies he deals with, all infra-red or ultra-violet or whatever. It was like a game. Doesn't seem quite such a laugh, now.

And what made Karl the main suspect?

Look at him. He's an oddball. You know, on the news, when they interview the neighbours of some nut, they all say "He was a very quiet chap, he kept himself to himself," that's Karl all over. The man's a librarian for God's sake! What sort of job is that for a grown man?

And what is your current employment?

How dare you! If Harry hadn't been such a churlish git and thrown me out just as all my hard work was starting to pay dividends, I'd be earning more in a month than you get all year!
I'm sorry. It's been a very difficult time for us all. I didn't mean that about Harry. He was a splendid cove, really.

Returning to the evening in question, were there any other arguments?

Well, Harry was always fond of putting the cat among the pigeons. He managed to upset most of them, not seriously, it was just his manner.

Did he do anything to upset you?

No. No, not really.

What did you do after Antonia cut herself?

I was never any good at the old first aid you see, so I left it to Randa and Desmond. They sent me off to find some brandy to calm her down.

Apparently this took you a long time.

Er...yes. Yes, it did. I was certain I had a bottle in my room somewhere but I couldn't find it anywhere. Found it eventually though.

Did you see Harry during this time?

No. He was in his room, with the door shut. I could hear him on the phone, though.

Could you tell who he was talking to?

No, one doesn't like to eavesdrop, does one old chap?

And who was downstairs when you returned?

Antonia was still there. She was a bit calmer, but still bleeding. Desmond was hugging her, which I'm not sure she was altogether too thrilled about. Shirley had gone off somewhere, and Randa was there for a while, but went off in search of clean bandages. She was gone for ages, and when she got back, at about 11 o'clock, Antonia went to the downstairs bathroom, to clean herself up. The brandy seemed to have worked a treat, as did the wash and brush-up. She was gone for about ten minutes and we started to worry about her but when she came back she was grinning like a Cheshire cat.

And she seemed stable?

I'm not sure that woman has ever seemed stable. But the strangest behaviour of the night came from Karl and Desmond.

Explain.

Well, five or so minutes after Antonia returned from the bathroom, smiling like a fiend, we all heard someone thunder up the stairs to the first floor. Desmond got up and said, "I'll just see if everything's OK" and disappeared off and then ten minutes later, we heard someone thundering down the stairs, and then we heard Karl shout "Vile yuppie scum!", and then the back door slammed.

The back door?

It had been open all evening, let the air in, get rid of all that awful garlic stuff Desmond had cooked up. Talking of Desmond, he came back downstairs after about ten minutes with his hands in his pockets, looking very sheepish, saying "Everything's fine" over and over again, very quietly. Then he had a drink and shut up.

Where did he go?

It had been open all evening, let the air in, get rid of all that awful garlic stuff Desmond had cooked up. Talking of Desmond, he came back downstairs after about ten minutes with his hands in his pockets, looking very sheepish, saying "Everything's fine" over and over again, very quietly. Then he had a drink and shut up.

Where did he go?

No idea. I doubt he went outside as Karl had slammed the door on his way out and it locks automatically. Anyhow, after a few minutes, Miranda went upstairs and you know the rest. Terrible business.

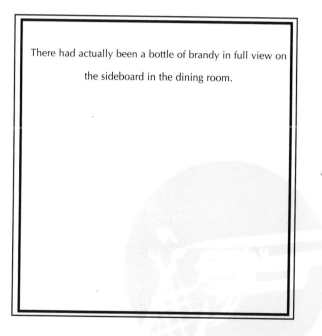

There had actually been a bottle of brandy in full view on the sideboard in the dining room.

33

Detective Inspector Rogers and Karl Wilson.

I understand the dinner party on the night in question was called to "patch things up" between the deceased and the others. What needed patching up between you two?

Nothing that was going to be sorted out by some poncey dinner party, that's for sure. Look, I think what happened was awful, I hope you get the person what done it, and it's not often I'm on the side of the police, but I have to say that he was a bloody horrible, malignant person.

Why do you feel this way?

He was a sadistic public school type. He spent half his time working hard to screw every last penny out of people less fortunate than himself, then he used to unwind by playing sick practical jokes on people.

Such as?

Him and that chinless wonder Antony, when they discovered I was a librarian, they spent about a week tearing up books and dropping the pages in front of my window, making paper planes out of them, even setting them on fire. Then I discovered that they were library books. Harry had actually sent Antony out to join the library, my library, just to destroy these books. Sick or what? If they didn't have anything to do, they'd just jump up and down on the floor at two in the morning, or play opera at top volume with the speakers pressed to the floor. Sick, like I said.

He was also your landlord, wasn't he?

Er, yes...in a way. When he bought the building off the Richardsons, he didn't realise that the long let agreement they'd given me meant that I was exempt from any changes in rent or contract he wanted to make. Ha, he thought he was so sharp, such a player, ripping off this sweet old couple who'd lived here all their lives, but he didn't spot this loophole. He's regretted it ever since.

On the night of the dinner party, you left when Antonia cut herself. Why?

I'd had enough. I'd had them all chattering away, then taunting Antonia about the death of her cat. I'd been caught between the Thruxtons alternating between droning on about themselves and snapping at each other. Then Antonia goes mental and turns into a drama queen, and everyone started fussing over her. I hadn't wanted to go in the first place, so I saw my opportunity and left.

Where did you go?

Down to my flat.

Out the front or the back?

The back.

And what did you do there?

I read a biography of Ho Chi Minh and I phoned Samantha, my partner. You can check with her, she'll tell you it's true.

I'm not accusing you of anything.

That'll be the day! A copper not trying to fit someone up!

Why did you return upstairs?

I'm sorry?

Why did you leave the house, go down to your flat, then come back to hurl insults?

What...er...no.

Are you denying that you returned to the ground floor flat, ran up the stairs to the first floor, ran down again, shouted "Vile yuppie scum" and then left, slamming the door?

It wasn't like that...I...they'd been really winding me up, not just tonight, but for a year and a half now. I went downstairs and I tried to calm down and I tried to read my book and I called Sam, BUT I WAS SO ANGRY! I thought my head was going to explode, so I went back up to the ground floor flat and shouted at them. Then I left. I didn't hurt anyone, I only shouted and then I slammed the door. I did do that, but I didn't hurt anyone.

What did you do upstairs?

I didn't go upstairs! I promise you!

Well, who did then?

I don't know!

Well, just before you admittedly shouted, someone was heard running upstairs to the first floor, and then coming down again.

It wasn't me! I didn't go upstairs!

OK. You said that you thought that Harry and Antony tormented you for fun. Can you think of any other reason why they would take such a dislike to you?

No. None.

Did Miranda adopt a similar attitude?

No, she was always polite. Quite sweet, really.

And what was your attitude to her?

What are you getting at? What have those bastards told you? It's all lies. All of it. And that's the truth. You have to believe me! Look, I lied before. I did go upstairs. I was going to have it out, once and for all, with Harry.

What happened?

Nothing. I burst into his study but he was on the phone. He didn't even turn round. He was just mumbling, I guess it was an intimate call because I couldn't hear a word, just sort of hushed mumblings.

What did you do?

I stood there and told him to put the phone down. He ignored me, no surprise there. I stood there for a bit, then ran down the stairs and shouted. It wasn't clever, I was just wound up. But I didn't hit him.

What time was this?

Twenty past eleven. On the wall above his desk Harry had this huge clock which was set to UK time and then lots of smaller ones underneath with the times in the countries he did busin...he exploited and polluted with yuppie tourism.

Miranda initially broke off her relationship with Harry because he was a serial philanderer. The night before the dinner party he told her he hadn't been near any other women since the break-up, so keen was he to get back with her.

Detective Inspector Rogers and Antonia Curbishley.

I understand you got very upset at the dinner party.

Upset? No. I got furious. I'm sure the others have portrayed me as some foolish neurotic woman, and yes, I made a bit of a scene, but I have no regrets. Apart from cutting myself, which was a silly accident. That amount of fury affects your aim you know.

So why were you so furious?

It's a bit of a saga. My cat, Smushy, I'd had him for years, he was more than a...whatever, I was very attached to him. Anyway, Smushy got run over about a month ago, which, well, you know, these things happen. I know that, but they're still very sad when they do. So I've been a bit upset about it, which is only natural. And then, literally adding insult to injury, Harry starts making jokes about it. He was such a spoilt brat of a man.

And these jokes made you angry?

To begin with, no, but when you've had some over-privileged sadist serving lasagne by dropping each portion onto the plate from a great height, then making a screeching noise and miaowing, I think most saints would have had their patience tried. Turned out that was just the beginning of the evening's entertainment.

Wasn't the idea of this meal to "patch up differences"?

I think that may have been his original intention, but that was quickly forgotten.

What differences did you have to patch up?

Oh, we'd had a long running battle about noise. I play the cello, and teach piano to children, and since Harry's set up business at home, he's been bothered by the noise. His office is directly beneath my music room, so he was in the front line. But instead of coming to some reasonable agreement, he just started to retaliate. He installed huge speakers in his study and would play music at top volume when I was playing. Or when I was asleep. Occasionally when the children were being dropped off or picked up by their parents, he'd hang out of the window, pulling faces and putting on this Quasimodo voice, shouting "She's mad! She's mad!". Charming, I'm sure you'd agree.

Did anything else stand out about the meal?

Well, Harry was being rude to everyone, so it's difficult to single
anything out. After a bit, you just switch off. One odd thing was
when Harry started going on about the peeping tom. I hadn't heard
anything about this, but obviously everyone else had. Harry was
saying that he'd captured the 'voyeur' on video or something, and
every time he said "peeping tom" he'd say it really loudly, and looked
around the table in this melodramatic manner.

Did he seem to focus on anyone in particular?

No, he was obviously relishing twisting the knife. Everyone just
smiled. I didn't know if the whole thing was just a joke, or whether
he was being completely serious. It was always difficult to tell with
Harry.

Anything else?

Not really. Oh, what am I saying? Ha! Harry sort of proposed to
Miranda. Everyone was stunned. I thought they'd been an item for
years, so I was surprised at the surprise, if you see what I mean. It
was only after talking to Antony afterwards that I found out that
they'd split up a while ago.

What did Miranda do when this happened?

She didn't say anything, she just smiled. I thought that maybe they'd
talked about it before, and this was just them announcing it. But
everyone else seemed a bit taken aback by it, apart from Karl, who
just carried on sneering. The weirdest thing was Shirley's reaction.
She looked like she'd been slapped with a wet fish.

Why did you cut yourself?

Well, I didn't do it deliberately if that's what you mean. I was just
furious and missed.

What time was this?

About 10.20pm. Harry and Karl left, I think, and Miranda and
Desmond looked after my hand. Antony went off somewhere, came
back ages later with a bottle of brandy. Desmond insisted on
hugging me, but I have to say that the brandy was far more
effective.

What time did you go to the bathroom?

Just after eleven, I think. I needed to clean all the blood off and pull myself together.

Did you see anyone else?

Not a soul.

And while you were in the bathroom, did you hear anything?

Not really. But when I came out I thought I heard someone go up the stairs but I wasn't really aware that I was going to be a witness in a murder investigation, so I didn't really give it much thought.

What happened between you getting back and the body being found?

Well, I got back, and about five minutes later Desmond went off to see who was making the racket on the stairs.

Did you notice anything odd about him when he came back?

Not really. I mean, he's normally quite odd. Quiet and odd. Come to think of it, he did have this line on his forehead, which could have been blood. I'm not pointing the finger. It could have been anything. I only spotted it after he had, in the mirror over the mantelpiece. He was cleaning it off with the palm of his hand, like he was smoothing his hair out of his eyes or something. Then Miranda went off and discovered the body.

Until the night of the party, nobody had picked up the
jade buddha statue for weeks.

Detective Inspector Rogers and Shirley Thruxton.

How well did you know the deceased?

Well...you know...we lived next door to each other. We saw each other in the street, occasionally we would pop round for something. We didn't socialise. We share the garden, but not the gardening, if you see what I mean.

Were you given any specific reason for the dinner party?

Not really. It was just everyone in the house, I suppose. I think they'd been having problems with their two tenants, you know, noise and so on.

But you hadn't had any arguments with them?

No. They're a little noisy, a bit cheeky, too, I suppose, Harry and Antony, but it's just high spirits. Besides, I'm out all day, and quite often work late at the office, so I miss a lot of it. Anyway, I think it's nice to hear people around you, if you're alone in the house. The cello is a bit annoying, but she's a nice girl that Antonia, always checking that it isn't too loud.

Tell me about the dinner party.

Mmm. The high spirits were a little too high. Harry had a captive audience and he was just being rude really. I'm not too fond of Karl, he's an awkward so-and-so at the best of times, but they were being terrible to him.

How?

Well, a lot of it seemed to be private jokes, either that or it went over my head, but at one point they seemed to be accusing him of being a sex pervert.

Had you been aware of a peeping tom?

No, not at all. I thought it may have been one of their public school pranks gone too far. Karl wasn't looking too happy, but I can't say I blame him. Even if he is some sort of lurker, well then he needs help, not people making fun of him in public.

Anything else notable about the meal?

Well, they gave Antonia an even harder ride. It was embarrassing. Then after all that nastiness, Harry says he's getting married.

Were you surprised at this?

Not at all. I guess that was the real reason for calling the dinner party, to let us all know. They'd been seeing each other for ages and ages. I mean, they'd had their differences, but first love and all that. How she puts up with him...sorry...put up with him, I don't....sorry. It's not right to speak like that of the dead.

What happened when Antonia cut her hand?

Well, Harry walked away from it, typical really. Karl got even more sneery and ran off, and Antony wondered off, vaguely looking for something to calm her down. He was gone for ages, so I said I thought I had seen some old sedatives somewhere in our house, and went through the garden to get them. Of course I had to look all over for them.

And then the phone rang?

You do do your homework, don't you? Yes, it did. Someone from one of the hotels I supply staff for, saying that a silver service waitress hadn't turned up for the late sitting. Happens every so often. I had to make a couple of calls, to find someone to cover. But one thing, before I forget, as I was searching for tranquillisers in my bedroom, I heard an almighty crash next door.

What time was this?

I'm not sure. No I know, it was just before 11pm, cos afterwards I remember hearing the clock in his office chime 11.

And what time did you return next door?

Oh about half an hour later. As I was coming through my kitchen, I heard someone come out of their kitchen and go down the steps to the basement.

Karl?

I suppose so, but I didn't actually see him, so I can't be sure. When

43

I got back, Antonia seemed to have stopped bleeding and had calmed down. She was chatting to Miranda and Antony. It was all a bit subdued though.

Was your husband there?

No, he wasn't, but he came back shortly after I got back. He'd heard Karl shouting or something and had been seeing what was going on.

Did he seem to be behaving oddly?

How do you mean? Desmond is very shy and he hates any sort of disturbance, so the whole evening had been a bit of a strain on him.

If he hates disturbance, how come he's got a record for it?

He'd been under a lot of pressure. I don't think that people who haven't worked in restaurant kitchens have any idea what a cut-throat business it can be. Some very unpleasant people are involved, you know.

Did you notice any blood on your husband or on his clothes?

At the time, no, but afterwards yes. He had been attending to a woman who had stabbed herself clean through the back of her hand don't forget. Look, you don't have to be an agony aunt to see that me and Desmond have some serious differences, but I do know him, and I know he'd be incapable of battering someone like Harry to death. I live with the man, and he'd have fallen apart with guilt by now.

Was your husband close to Harry?

Not really. They didn't have much in common.

So why did your husband cook the meal for him?

I didn't know that. Erm...Desmond likes to cook, you know. He had lost his job and cooking dinner for Harry gave him the opportunity to do what he enjoys most.

In the bottom of Harry's bin, under weeks' worth of debris,

are a couple of newspapers with lots of letters cut out.

Detective Inspector Rogers and Desmond Thruxton.

You prepared the meal on the night in question. Why?

Harry was terrible in the kitchen. He doesn't understand food.

Had you cooked for him before?

No.

So why did you do it this time?

He suggested it and I agreed.

As simple as that?

Yes.

Were you surprised by Harry's proposal to Miranda?

It did seem a little odd. They never struck me as being well-suited.

But you don't know them particularly well?

No, I don't. You asked for my opinion and I gave it to you. You don't have to be intimate with someone to have an opinion of them.

How often did you speak to Harry?

Hardly ever. Pleasantries in the garden, that sort of thing. He seemed quite a character though, from what I saw of him.

And Miranda?

Even less. Again, she seemed nice. But very different to Harry.

On the evening in question, you helped Antonia after her accident?

Yes. In kitchens it happens all the time. She was upset enough before she did it. She just needed a bit of reassurance and a bit of warmth.

As well as a tourniquet?

Miranda seemed much more knowledgeable about that sort of thing. Between us we made a good team, I think.

Was Miranda with you all the time?

No she went off for a bit. In search of a tourniquet, come to think of it.

Was she gone long?

Yes. It seemed like ages, but she was back at just after 11pm, so it could only have been about 15 or 16 minutes.

Have you any idea where she went?

I told you she went to find a tourniquet. She looked downstairs, and then she went upstairs. All she could find was an old tea-towel.

In quarter of an hour's searching, upstairs and downstairs, the best she could do was an old tea-towel? Don't you think that's a bit strange?

No. It wasn't really that urgent. The first one was doing OK, Antonia seemed to be relaxing, we were chatting. By the time she came back, I'd almost forgotten what she went off for in the first place.

Your wife was absent for much of this.

She got caught up next door. Work phoned up, you see. She works very hard. She was back when I came downstairs after looking for Karl.

How did you know it was Karl?

I heard someone go thundering up the stairs and went to see who it was. When I came back down the others said it must've been Karl for while I was upstairs, he had charged down the stairs, shouted a volley of abuse and then left, slamming the back door behind him.

What did you do upstairs?

I looked around and everything seemed OK, so I came back down again.

You say everything was OK; was the door to Harry's study open?

No, it wasn't.

How did you know which room was Harry's study? You said earlier you were little more than nodding acquaintances.

When Miranda discovered the body, we all went to see. When I was up there, I looked in all the rooms with open doors, and none of those had Harry in them, so I presumed his was one of the rooms with a shut door.

So you didn't see anyone upstairs?

No. Karl had already run out - to his flat, I think. Shirley said she heard someone going down there. Nobody else would want to go there, would they?

A witness said she thought she saw you wiping blood from your face after you returned downstairs.

That's perfectly possible. I had been attending to a woman who had stabbed herself clean through the back of her hand. You must remember that, even before Miranda found poor Harry, it was a mad, manic evening, with tears, blood and shouting. It wasn't just a run of the mill dinner party you understand.

Desmond washed his hands before going up to see who had run up the stairs like a madman.

notes

D.I. Rogers' Notes following first interviews

Dinner party - very ambitious, none of guests knew their neighbours very well - there had obviously been some tension between landlord and tenants
Harry Hilton - fun-loving but spoilt young man - practical jokes edged on cruel and even sadistic. More than one guest bore the brunt of his taunts. Could that have been reason enough to kill him?
Everyone left dining room at some time; everyone a suspect

Miranda Davies:

No immediate motive yet she took a long time to find a tea-towel

Antony Croton:

A friend and flatmate but took ages to find brandy. Why?

Antonia Curbishley:

Clearly unbalanced and certainly provoked but capable of murder???

Desmond Thruxton:

Upstairs for nearly ten minutes - doing what? Blood on forehead?

Shirley Thruxton:

Said she wasn't surprised at Harry's announcement of his engagement -

others said she was. Heard crash - in Harry's study?

Karl Wilson:

Commie. Hated Hilton. Defensive during interview - lying? Peeping Tom?

TO DO:

Get character reference on Karl Wilson

Order print-out of all calls made to and from house on night of 29/8/96

Phone lines:

Hilton (home)	01622 - 436 8764
Hilton (business)	01622 - 436 2547
Karl Wilson	01622 - 435 3968
Shirley Thruxton	01622 - 436 7465

Scene of Crime Report 2

Forensic Report & Scene-Of-Crime Analysis

Update

Date:	29th August
Time on scene:	23:55hrs
Offence:	Murder.
Victim:	Harold Bertram Hilton, male, 31 yrs.
Perpetrator:	Unknown.
Location:	59 Kippax Grove, Forley FW4 8UG.

Description:
Suspected murder weapon is jade statuette of Buddha found on the floor behind the victim. Impact markings favour throwing rather than dropping. Fragments of jade found outside the open door. Again no clear prints.
Red leather collar, from a black-haired cat, bearing a name disc ("Smushy") found just outside the door.
No clear fingerprints.
In addition to the substantial wounding caused by blows to the back and top of the head, there was a small wound on forehead,

caused by pen in holder on desk.
Haemorrhaging pattern suggests minor wound
occurred twenty minutes after what turned
out to be the fatal blows to the back of
the head.
Drawers in the desk were opened and appear
to have been rifled through. Cheque book,
credit cards and over £1,500 in various
currencies were all in full view, but were
left intact.
A video camera had been knocked off its
tripod, next to the deceased's desk.

Conclusions:

Robbery not an immediate motive. 20
minutes between fatal attack and wounding
of the forehead. Presumably victim
remained immobile in upright position and
then fell forward. This could have been
caused by spontaneous post-traumatic muscle
contraction or the body could have been
disturbed during search of desk.

Officer on Scene:

Det.Insp. Ken Rogers

Report compiled by: Dr Susan Timmins

For the past few weeks, Smushy's collar had been hanging round the neck of the Buddha statue on the stairs.

**Detective Inspector Rogers and
Miranda Davies.**

Are you familiar with a jade Buddha statue?

Oh...I mean...yes.

Where did it normally live?

For the past few months, it's been on the stairs. It used to
be on the mantelpiece in the sitting room, but Harry took it
down, when...he and I split up..I mean...fell out.

Have you handled it recently?

No. No, why should I?

You hesitated when I mentioned it. Why?

No reas...it's just that...has this got anything to do with
Antonia?

Why should it?

It's a long story. Harry bet Tony £50 that he didn't have
enough guts to run over Antonia's cat. This was all part of
Harry's war of attrition over noise. So one day Tony walks
in, holding this collar. Harry thought this was the funniest
thing he'd ever seen, gave Tony the money and then
chucked the collar over the head of this Buddha. He'd
make this stupid miaowing noise every time he went past
it on the stairs.

He made no effort to hide it, what with Antonia coming round?

Of course not. He thrived on that sort of antagonism.

Did she see it?

I've no idea. Why were you asking about the statue?

We're fairly sure that it was the murder weapon. We're waiting for fingerprint results, so we just need to know who might have touched it. Can you think of any reason why Harry proposing to you might have upset Antony?

Yes, I can. Look, I was really silly. When Harry and I split up, there was...well, put it this way, me and Tony got drunk a couple of times, both complaining about Harry, and one thing led to another. Anyone with half a brain could have seen that it was just one of those on-the-rebound things. Sadly, this is Tony we're talking about here. He thought that this was it, he'd finally found love. Tonight must have been terrible for him.

Did he often argue with Harry?

No. Never. Harry would bully him and humiliate him, and Tony would just run back, like a dog. He may be stupid though, but he's not completely insensitive. It was all building up. Every now and again he'd get drunk and cry on my shoulder about how mean Harry was.

Harry sacking him was the last straw. Anyone else would have moved out, got a proper job, but Tony just doesn't have that sort of self-reliance.

Can we go back to the time you spent looking for dressings for Antonia's wound. Did you hear a loud crash or any other sort of noise?

No. No, I didn't. I mean, I don't remember hearing one.

Did you notice anything unusual around the door to Harry's study on your travels?

No. But I wasn't really looking. I was in a hurry.

Finally, is there any reason, any reason that you haven't told me, why you should have felt angry towards Harry, any disagreements or suchlike?

No! Who said there was? Who's been saying these things? Is it that poisonous old cow from next door? Always getting involved in things that she shouldn't.

It was only a question. As long as you're sure there's nothing more you want to tell me?

Look, I've just remembered. I did handle that statue the morning of the dinner party. I was cleaning and I had to pick it up, so my fingerprints will be on it as well.

Harry had become quite absorbed with the hunt for the peeping tom. Getting his hands on some infra-red video equipment, used by a contact for night safaris, allowed him to capture something on tape that caused him to change his mind as to the identity of the stalker.

Detective Inspector Rogers and Antony Croton.

Have you got any idea why I've called you back for a second chat?

No, not really. I thought it was probably the form in this sort of thing.

I've been looking at what you said, and at what the other witnesses have said, and everything doesn't quite tie up. You were upstairs for a long period of time looking for that bottle of brandy. Are you sure you only went into your bedroom?

Yes I'm sure. Now look here Detective Inspector I think you are barking up the wrong tree hounding us, maybe it was someone else who killed Harry. You know, a passing madman, or a cat burglar or something.

Well, robbery is out of the question. As far as we can establish, nothing was stolen, and there was a lot up there for the taking. Also, no-one saw or heard the front door opening all evening. Tell me, does anyone else have a set of keys, besides you and Miranda. A neighbour perhaps?

No. The only spare set are the "crush keys". Harry christened them that, he said they were especially for lovers and mistresses and so on. When we first moved in, if I was going out Harry'd say "Are you taking the crush keys?". We never actually used them though. They're still hanging in the hall. Anyhow, someone could have got in through the garden and then through the back door.

No one other than the seven of you was seen or heard at any stage in the evening.

Aha, but if you look at where everyone was, in the dining room, looking after Antonia, you can only see a bit of the garden through the French windows. Anyone could have gone in through the back door and up the stairs without anyone being any the wiser. Any passing loon could have got in and done it. Go and track them down instead of harassing Harry's friends and neighbours!

I shall take note of your opinions. Getting back to the investigation, did you see Harry at all while you were looking for that bottle of brandy?

Well, I've already told you, I heard Harry on the phone.

So you heard him but you did not see him.

OK, OK, I confess, I did go in to talk to Harry. Actually we had a bit of an argument.

What was the subject of the argument?

Oh, the whole thing. I've been a bit...unsettled. You know, flitting from one thing to another without, to be honest, too much success. Getting binned by the army, particularly out of Pa's old regiment was the last straw really. Father threatened to redirect my trust fund if I didn't stick at something. So when Harry set up Exclusively Jet Set, his travel company, he took me on. Then, just as it starts to get going, and just as I start to feel like I know what I'm doing, and where everything is, and I'm starting to enjoy myself, Harry tells me that it's not working, that he'll have to "down-size the operation", and that he's going to do everything himself. He gives me a month's pay and that's it. Nothing to show for all my hard work. And then...

I understand that this could give you cause to argue, but why did it come to a head on this particular evening?

Because...because it just did. All the business with Exclusively Jet Set was just typical of the way he always brushed me...brushed everyone aside.

But from what you've said before, you actively helped him brush people aside, so that can't have been the trigger in this case. Also, in our previous chat, you didn't mention anything about Harry's proposal to Miranda. Why not?

(silence)

Was that the real cause of your argument? I have talked to Miranda about this, you know.

Did she tell you everything? I...it was...they didn't tell me anything. I knew there was no future in it, it was doomed to failure, like everything I do. Give me something good, you can be sure I'll foul it up.

Be that as it may, what went on between you and Harry?

After hearing their announcement, I was so angry I knew I had to have a go at Harry. The first chance I could, I went into his office, when I was off looking for this bottle of brandy, and had a blazing row with him. You see, I'm not sure if he proposed to Miranda just to spite me. It sounds ridiculous, I know, the last cry from the scaffold, but it was the sort of thing that Harry was capable of.

Why did you lie?

The whole thing really upset me. It still upsets me. I wasn't the only one either. The expression on Drab Shirley's face when she heard the proposal was priceless. Bit of a crush there. Or more. Who knows? Harry was capable of anything. Given Randa's expression when she saw Shirley's face, she thought he was capable of anything as well.

Did you resolve the argument with Harry?

Ironically, yes. He pointed out that I'd been fooling around with his first love, and his wife-to-be, and I should be grateful that he hadn't kicked me out of the house the moment he found out. Seemed fair enough I suppose. I hadn't really thought about it in those terms before.

On your way up the stairs, was the jade Buddha still on the stairs?

No idea, old chap, I'm afraid. I was seeing red on the way up. I'm fairly sure it was there on the way down, though. Why do you ask?

It was the murder weapon.

What, the old "lord of love"? He was some Vietnamese love charm Randa brought back for Harry when they first met. And he killed him. Shocking, eh?

Miranda is Harry's solicitor. It was her who drew up the agreement that made Antony's £5,000 investment in Exclusive Jet Set strictly non-refundable. She has recently been working on, and knows the entire contents of, the deceased's will.

Forley Public Library
Geoff Street
Forley

Dear Det Insp Rogers,

In response to your request for information regarding Karl Wilson, an employee of four years standing, all I can say is that he has a good work record, he was very open about his history of convictions, and is popular with colleagues and the public alike. Occasionally he has got a little heated in debate with colleagues, on one occasion so much so that I had to recommend he take the rest of the day off to calm down. Apart from that, he is a hard-working and diligent member of staff, willing to take on responsibility. He is also the staff union spokesman.

Normally, I would have ignored the following information, but given the extreme nature of your enquiry, I think I would be ignoring my duty if I didn't inform you. I received the following in an envelope with a Forley postmark three weeks ago. I have not informed Karl about this, having dismissed it as a hoax or a malicious prank. However, I did, somewhat to my shame, keep a closer eye on Karl after receiving it, and saw no evidence whatsoever of the allegations.

If I can be of any more help, please don't hesitate to contact me.

Yours sincerely

Keith Curle

Keith Curle
Head Librarian

KarL wilson
is **A** PERVERT.

And a peeping Tom

i have p**R**oo**F**

Sack him

before

he hurts **someone**

A friend

If the prints from the jade Buddha had been any clearer, they would have revealed that two people had handled it on the night of the dinner.

Detective Inspector Rogers and Karl Wilson.

I'd like to say, before you begin, that I've co-operated thus far, but that I consider this police harassment a violation of my civil rights.

Your objections have been added to the record. All I can say is that this is an investigation of the utmost seriousness, and given various pieces of evidence that have arisen since our previous talk, I considered a second interview essential to gain a clear picture of your movements on the night in question. You said earlier that when you entered Harry Hilton's study, he was talking on the phone.

That's right.

And that he ignored you.

That's right.

Did you hear anything he actually said?

No. Like I said before, he was just murmuring.

Are you sure he was actually talking?

What? Look, I didn't hang around. He didn't move a muscle when I came in. I wasn't going to hang about. I may be a socialist, but I'm not given to banging my head against a brick wall every minute of every day.

How well lit was the room?

What is this about? Look, I was furious, I was looking for a fight, so odd as it may seem, I'd left my light meter at home.

Was the overhead light on?

No. Just the one on the desk.

So Harry was between you and the light?

Yes. The light was one of those bendy ones, right down over the desk.

On your way upstairs, did you see a green jade Buddha on the stairs?

Look. I dunno what you're getting at, but no, I didn't see any statues, I didn't make detailed notes of the lighting arrangements, I couldn't give you the reference number for the nicely-bourgeois pastel paint on the walls, I just went up there in a huff, I came down in a huff, I stupidly shouted something, and then I went home. I didn't kill anyone.

But you just said you went up there looking for a fight.

A slip of the tongue. Obviously I wasn't going to have a scrap with him.

Is there anything you haven't told us about your relationship with Harry?

"Relationship" is a bit of a grand word for it. Particularly coming from a copper.

One of the witnesses said that at dinner, Harry was hinting that you were a peeping tom.

(silence)

69

I'm not repeating that allegation. I'm looking for a murderer. All I need to know from you is whether Harry had accused you of this, and the extent of the accusation.

I've said all I'm going to say. You said you wanted to know about my movements on the night in question, and I'll answer questions about that. Anything else and I want a solicitor with me.

Fair enough. Is there anything else you can tell me about your visit to Harry's study?

No. I've been through all this before. I did...I...when I was leaving the study I thought I'd smashed the door. After I closed the door, I saw this small dent, about head height.

But nothing in the door way. No object on the floor?

Not as far as I could see. I really can't tell you any more than that.

Although the spare set of front door keys had not been used, there is a set of keys for the back door that neither Miranda nor Antony know about. They were used on the night in question and had been used frequently in the preceding months.

FORLEY C.I.D.

SEARCH WARRANT REPORT

Address:

Basement flat, 59 Kippax Grove, Forley, FW4
8UG

Name of occupant:

Karl Malcolm Wilson

Crime under investigation:

Murder/Theft FCID 455823, HBH

Issuing officer:

Dr B.J.Carter, J.P.

Investigating officer:

Det Insp K. Rogers

Date of search:

31/08/96

Report:

Myself and three other officers, using keys supplied by the occupant's landlord (the victim) via his ex-girlfriend, entered the premises. The occupant was not in evidence. Nothing belonging to the victim or the victim's household was found after a thorough search. Possibly relating to the crime was a file, presumably maintained by the accused, which documented what seems to be a campaign of threats, intimidation and/or blackmail. Sample included on the following page.

Move out

now,

or your boSs,
your family

and your Commie
friends will learn all about

your little night time excursions.

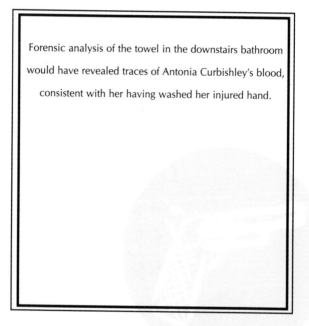

Forensic analysis of the towel in the downstairs bathroom would have revealed traces of Antonia Curbishley's blood, consistent with her having washed her injured hand.

alpurc

DIGITAL COMMUNICATIONS

DETAILED CALL ANALYSIS

SECURITY CLEARANCE 557833 POLICE ACCESS

DATE   **29/08/96**
POST   **22:00hrs**

CALLS TO/FROM ACCOUNT #56-299/6JV 00QW -
HARRY HILTON

BUSINESS LINE NO.   **01622 - 436 2547**
OUTGOING CALLS   **0**
INCOMING CALL   **1**
CALLER NO.   **01622 - 436 7465**
CONNECTION: **22:35hrs**
TERMINATION: **23:20hrs**

*signal activity analysis reveals that although line was connected from 22:35hrs to 23:20hrs, there was no line activity between 23:07hrs and 23:20hrs.

CALLS TO/FROM ACCOUNT #56-299/6JV 00QW -
HARRY HILTON

HOME LINE NO.   **01622 - 436 8764**

OUTGOING CALL   **1**
Attempted at 22:36hrs, caller engaged, no connection made.

INCOMING CALLS   **0**

CALLS TO/FROM ACCOUNT #76-449/6JV 01DW -
KARL WILSON

HOME LINE NO.   **01622 - 435 3968**
OUTGOING CALL   **1**
INCOMING CALLS   **0**
CALLER NUMBER: **0171 654 7865**
CONNECTION: **22:59hrs**
TERMINATION: **23:18hrs**

*signal activity analysis reveals line activity between
22:59hrs and 23:18hrs.

END OF REPORT

One purely practical argument Harry used to woo Miranda back to him was that now he was working at home, he wouldn't come into contact with anybody with whom he could be unfaithful to her.

**Detective Inspector Rogers and
Shirley Thruxton.**

Interview carried out at the request of Shirley Thruxton.

It's about my husband. He's had...he's in hospital. In a
psychiatric hospital.

What happened?

I came home from work the other day and I found him in
the front room. He was sitting on the floor, he'd wrapped
himself in some sort of brown tape, not like sticky tape, you
understand, but like in video tapes, and we haven't even got
a video, and he had found lots of pencils, chopped them up
into tiny pieces, and arranged them in patterns around him. I
never knew we had so many pencils.

Anything else?

There were...God, this is so embarrassing...there were bits of
underwear. Not my underwear. I cleared that away before
the ambulance came to get him.

What have the doctors said?

That he's had a comprehensive mental breakdown.

How much of a surprise was this?

Not much, to be honest. Me and Desmond have been growing apart for some time, mainly because he's become very withdrawn, which coincided with him getting sacked all the time.

What did he get sacked for?

He always said it was because they didn't understand him, or "personality differences". But, and this isn't me spying, I was just worried about him, I asked around, being in the trade. No one wanted to talk about it. Eventually an old friend told me that it was impossible to have Desmond in the same kitchen as women. He'd stop concentrating on his work, he'd get uncomfortably close to them, ask them all sorts of questions. You can imagine.

Have you seen him in hospital yet?

Yes. It was terrible. He didn't recognise me. He kept on screaming about blood, lots of blood. He looked awful. He's been stabbing himself in the forehead with pens and pencils. All the staff have to remove all their pens when they approach him. He's under heavy sedation. The doctors say it'll be a while before they're able to start any meaningful therapy. They did ask me if Des had a history of wounding himself or anyone else with pens. But it said in the paper that Harry was hit with a blunt instrument. It's all so horrible.

So you think your husband could have killed Harry Hilton?

Well, he was mad, wasn't he? He's not Desmond, not the Desmond I knew. It's awful. It's all too awful. I don't want to talk about it any more. I'm sorry, but I can't.

(Interview terminated due to distressed state of interviewee.)

84

Detailed metallurgical tests revealed that the spare set of front door keys had not been used on the night in question, or indeed for several months.

D.I. Rogers' Notes

All but one in the house admitted they went upstairs

Statue - Miranda Davies only one to admit she touched it

Send to forensic to find out who other prints belong to

Who had key to back door?

Dent on study door - how did it get there?

What caused Desmond's breakdown - significance of video and pens

and pencils?

Were Harry and Shirley having an affair?

Peeping tom - not Karl Wilson?

Who did Antonia Curbishley hear going up the stairs?

Someone went upstairs before Karl Wilson?

Key is in timing - Body found dead at 23:35hrs. Killed as a result

of fatal wounding to head - didn't die instantaneously - 20 minutes

later body received minor injury to forehead - disturbed by

someone searching study for something? Who and what? Murder

must have been at least 20 minutes before discovery of body. On

'phone until 23:07hrs.

Who had access?

CONCLUSION

Here end the rather messy files of Detective Inspector Rogers. They contain all the necessary information to identify the murderer, as well as several false clues and dead ends. It's time to decide whodunit but before you turn over, think of your promotion and your reputation, both of which depend on your ability to solve this crime.

Check through your notes carefully, comparing them to those of D.I. Rogers.

(The first solution page is in mirror-writing, to stop an accidental glance ruining the book - hold the book up to a mirror when you turn the page, and all will be revealed!)

DON'T TURN THE PAGE-

unless you want to know the solution!

SOLUTION

Shirley Thruxton was the murderer.

As her marriage to Desmond deteriorated, Shirley developed a "thing" for younger men and had been having an affair with Harry for the past four or five months. She had the back door keys to Harry's flat and came round for a "passionate rendezvous," whenever she got the opportunity. With Harry working from home and her able to pretend to be away on business, there were plenty such "opportunities," and Harry had strung her along, using Miranda's imminent departure from the flat as an indication that they had some sort of future together. Passionately in love with Harry, Shirley was shocked to the core when Harry announced his engagement to Miranda at the dinner table. In spite of trying to act nonchalantly when quizzed on the subject by Detective Inspector Rogers, neither Antony, nor Antonia nor Miranda failed to see her expression of horror. The out-of-the-blue announcement, coupled with her own failing marriage and her husband's downward spiral into psycho-sexual confusion, pushed her into taking drastic action.

PROCESS OF DEDUCTION:

Working out who did what and when, and who had access to the victim, are critical in order to work out who killed Harry.

From the analysis of phone calls made to and from 59 Kippax Grove on the night in question, we know that Harry was alive up until 11.07pm because his business telephone line was active. Harry's body was found at 11.35pm and at least 20 minutes had passed between his receiving several fatal blows and the body hitting the desk (see Scene of Crime Analysis Update). The murder must therefore have taken place between 11.07pm and 11.15pm.

Who had access to Harry in that time?

We can eliminate **Antony Croton** from the suspect list since he went upstairs at around 10.25pm and returned downstairs within ten minutes. He did not go back upstairs again until after Harry Hilton had been found dead.

Miranda Davies can also be discounted since we know that although she had gone upstairs to look for a tourniquet for Antonia, she returned to the dining room at 11pm and did not leave the dining room between then and discovering Harry's body at 11.35pm.

Antonia Curbishley did go to the bathroom after Miranda dressed her wound sometime soon after 11.00pm. But, as you are told, it was not the upstairs bathroom - it was downstairs. This was confirmed by Antony and by the presence of her own blood on the towels in the downstairs bathroom. She returned to the dining room ten minutes later. She was the only suspect not to go upstairs at any time.

Karl Wilson had gone down to his flat at 10.20pm. The 'phone records confirm that he was on the 'phone (to his girlfriend) from 10.59pm until 11.18pm. He returned at 11.20pm. He could not have committed the murder.

Finally **Desmond Thruxton** was in the dining room the entire time until he followed Karl up the stairs at 11.20pm - and we already know that the murder occurred before this time.

Shirley Thruxton's movements are unaccounted for between 11.07pm (when the 'phone line stops been actively used) and when she returned to the dining room just after 11.20pm. She was therefore the only person with access at the critical time.

FURTHER INFORMATION

Antony Croton may have wanted to kill Harry for being such a bully, for sacking him and for announcing his engagement to Miranda, with whom he was in love. He took such a long time looking for the brandy bottle because, as he eventually admitted, he did go into Harry's study, where he argued with Harry about Miranda. He was lying when he said he had heard Harry on the phone - as he later admitted.

Miranda Davies had good reason to kill Harry - she had a pathological hatred of being deceived. When she saw Shirley's expression when Harry announced their engagement, she realised he had been fooling around again despite promising her otherwise. She had warned him that if he ever lied to her again he would be "incredibly stupid and unreservedly sorry". She had gone to look for a tourniquet for Antonia - she said she had gone into the kitchen and the upstairs bathroom, where she found an old tea-towel in the airing cupboard. What she omitted to tell Detective Inspector Rogers was that she had picked up the jade Buddha statue, which had been a token of their love, and thrown it at Harry's closed study door in a fit of pique at his indiscretions (this was the crash Shirley heard from her bedroom). But as the clue said, there were more than one set of prints on the jade statue, and we know from the timings that she could not have killed Harry.

Antonia Curbishley - Harry had been very cruel to her about her beloved Smushy. However, she was in the downstairs bathroom or the dining room during the critical time. From the floor plan it is apparent that it would have been quite obvious to anyone in the dining room if she had in fact gone upstairs, and other evidence (see above) confirms her presence downstairs.

Shirley Thruxton, however, went next door to her flat around 10.34pm (seconds before Antony returned with the brandy at 10.35pm). She telephoned Harry on his work number at 10.35pm to try to persuade him to change his mind about marrying Miranda (see alpurc call analysis). Harry was patronising, refusing to relent or argue, which infuriated her further and at 11.07pm she (untruthfully) tells Harry to hang on as someone is at her door. What she really did was go out into the garden and enter Harry's flat unobserved via the open back door. She climbed the stairs and went into his study where she hit him several times on the back of the head with the first thing that came to hand, the jade 'lord of love' statue which she had found in the hallway outside his study door. Harry remained upright and rigid but he was fatally wounded and realising what she had done, Shirley rushed home the way she had come to start covering her tracks. She replaced the telephone receiver and calmly made her way back to Number 59 to rejoin everyone in the dining room. En route, she saw someone (Karl) go out of the back door down the stairs to the basement. As he slammed the back door in his wake, Shirley had to use the spare set of back door keys to let herself in. Nobody commented on the fact that she returned empty-handed, despite having been next door on a mission of some urgency for just under an hour.

Karl Wilson could've wanted to kill Harry because he not only thought him Bourgeois but he had to put up with Harry's endless taunts, his false accusations and his sick threats (Harry had been trying to force him out of the basement flat). As he eventually admitted to Detective Inspector Rogers, he did storm into Harry's study around 11.20pm (while Shirley was back disconnecting her telephone call). Once inside, the position of the light and the high-backed chair Harry was in made him think that Harry was mumbling affectionately down the phone to someone, ignoring him on purpose. In fact, Harry was barely alive, moaning for help. Furious at being ignored, Karl had fled the house screaming "vile yuppie scum" and slamming the back door shut behind him.

Finally **Desmond Thruxton** could have wanted to kill the deceased because Harry had found out it was he not Karl who was snooping on Miranda. As Shirley had hinted, when asked why Desmond kept being sacked, her husband was obsessed by other women (note Antony's observation that he was hugging the injured Antonia). While upstairs (he followed Karl up around 11.20pm), he used the pretext of looking for Karl, but he was really searching for Harry. He was keen to "negotiate" the return of the video evidence which revealed the identity of the peeping tom. He had cooked dinner as Harry had asked and hoped he would see reason and return the video in exchange. On finding Harry dead (or so he thought) when he eventually found him in his study, Desmond frantically searched the room for the video, knocking Harry's camera off its tripod in the process. In an attempt to search through the desk drawers, Desmond had managed to knock Harry, causing him to fall forwards onto the desk, a pen piercing his forehead in the process. Horrified at what he had done, Desmond grabbed the video, which was sitting in the top right hand drawer of the desk, stuffed it under his chef's apron, and ran downstairs arriving in the dining room around 11.30pm. He had indeed got blood on his forehead as Antonia suggested, and knowing he washed his hands on the way up the stairs, it must have got there as a result of contact with Harry. His breakdown, when he winds himself up in the video tape he found in Harry's study and chops pencils in two, is another clue that he witnessed Harry's horrendous dying state. In fact, the couple of minutes he spent in the room with Harry were enough to send him deep into the throes of madness.